H₂O and all that

H$_2$O

and all that

Martyn Berry

Sainsbury Publishing

First published by Heinemann Educational Books Ltd., 1980,
Reprinted 1981.

This edition by Sainsbury Publishing Ltd.
Auldearn, Main Street, Bleasby, Notts. NG14 7GH

British Library Cataloguing in Publication Data
H_2O and all that.
1. Humorous Prose.
I. Title II. Berry, Martyn, *1938–*
828.91407080356

ISBN   1-870-655-05-2

Typeset by **BKT Information Services**, Nottingham
Printed by **AthenæumPress Ltd**, Newcastle-upon-Tyne

O God of laughter, help me to be brave

and know a grim-set face is rarely right:

that gravity will drag me to the grave

while levity may lift me to the light.

Contents

Acknowledgements

I wish to thank:

Mike Peyton for his splendidly inimitable illustrations, and (with Kathleen) for hospitality and good walking; several colleagues for passing on to me a total of about one dozen of the choicer items; Graham Taylor and Katherine Ross of HEB for much help and advice; and my wife and children for their forbearance, as always. (At least they got a bit more amusement out of this one).

Preface to Second Edition

This is not the place to comment on the great, and not always beneficial, changes in the educational scene which have occurred during the 1980s. Nor shall I state my feelings about the potential disappearance of school chemistry into the black hole of so-called Balanced Science, or about the horrifically low level of recruitment of chemistry graduates as teachers.

Since the first edition of this – *er* – book, O level has gone; GCSE now thrives, as a result of immense labours by dedicated teachers, but perhaps only for a few more years before it is submerged beneath the National Curriculum, Records of Achievement, and no doubt further paper-intensive initiatives as yet unborn.

But the content of this little book is timeless. I have taken the opportunity to tidy up a few errors and add a couple of dozen items of recent collection, but that is all.

I am deeply grateful to George Sainsbury for causing the re-appearance of a volume which, judging from their letters and comments, gave many people much enjoyment; and, in doing so, raised a tidy sum for the Benevolent Fund of the Royal Society of Chemistry. We sincerely hope that this new edition will again achieve both results.

Preface

The title and tenor of this book owe much to the seminal work of those two great innovators, Walter Carruthers Sellar and Robert Julian Yeatman. Education, as they might have observed had they not been so unfortunate as to be historians, may be defined (in a semi-quantitive sense only) as the residue left when all the volatile components have evaporated. A rather forced kind of distillation is achieved by examination; some would describe it as distillation *in vacuo*. Nearly all the material in this book has been collected from the more viscous fractions of the many thousands of GCE O-level scripts which I have marked during the last fifteen years. Indeed, its collection has often provided a precious life-line to comparative sanity as midnights pass, deadlines approach, and piles of unmarked scripts grow never less.

There is no limit to the creative ingenuity of the youthful mind when under moderate pressure. Plain ignorance is sometimes funny, but often the laughter is tinged with sadness. Misunderstanding, resourcefully disguised or developed in the attempt to bamboozle the examiner, is usually very funny indeed. Slips of the pen and sudden failures of vocabulary, common to us all, can induce hilarity – as Gobfrey Shrdlu has shown many times.

This collection is intended for enjoyment. If some teachers and their customers use it as an Awful Warning, so be it. It may be that discussion of *why* a particular item is funny might even help to establish the (possibly) duller and more correct ideas and responses…

The evil rumour that a good honours degree in chemistry is needed in order to appreciate everything here is a base fabrication spread by my fourth formers. An O-level standard of chemical knowledge would help, but is certainly not essential.

And if you think that any item is the sort you might yourself have produced (or may well produce) in your own examination days – well then, you too may have gladdened, or may yet gladden, the heart of a poor old examiner sweating over his twice-yearly graft.

Martyn Berry

Introduction

With very few exceptions, all the following items were carefully copied by myself *verbatim* (so to speak) from GCE scripts. One or two have been slightly condensed; the – *er* – 'sense' has not been altered in any way. A brief indication of the question or an explanation has been provided for some items. In the very first item, the names have been changed. The material is arranged in a loose (an *extremely* loose) 'topic' form.

As an examiner, I deplore the fact that some candidates are entered for the examination without proper preparation, and that many more find difficulties in spelling, punctuation, and grammar. But, if we all knew what we were talking or writing about and said or wrote exactly what we meant, life would be far less interesting.

Let anyone who is without sin cast the first stone.

MYSELF: "Now – what does that thermometer read?"
PUPIL: "Tolstoy"

WARNING

For full effect some of these items should be read at least twice.

Or maybe not.

Dear Examiner...

Dear Examiner, I really would not bother to go any further. I'm afraid chemistry and I just do *not* mix. I tried telling my teacher but it would not have done him any good, nice though he is. I'm sorry to have wasted so much of your time, and mine too come to that.

Belinda would, she's just had to be taken out to be sick. Disgusting – everybody can hear the noise. She's going out again. They ought to put people down like her. They're worried about another girl behind me. Yes, she too is being helped out. Funny how it's never the boys.

If I pass all the others I'll get 7 O-levels.

Connie is coming down next week-end to see Mummy's nursery school, she'll enjoy that, and so shall I. If she stays for the week she'll be able to come to Melissa's and my dinner-party which also means we'll have to find another boy.

Heaven's time is going slowly. I've got biology tomorrow and the day after with history on Thursday. Then it's all over. 2.20 bell's gone.

Daddy's in Chicargo at the moment. He's coming home tomorrow night. He thinks I'm going to pass all my exams, including chemistry! Poor mis-led man.

I would like to thank you in advance about incenvenience caused by my spellings or the grammer.

Examiner. Next time ask some questions that are in the syllabus instead of this rubbish which I have never heard of.
Goodbye, sincerely, Ian.
[This was accompanied by a perfectly drawn weeping eye, life-size].

In 7 g of X there are Blast I can't answer it.

Let me first have the pleasure to demonstrate the allotropes of carbon.

Green solid has to be potassium as it is the most unusual element. How often do you see pink elephants?

It only has one electron at its outer most shell and therefore it readily reacts. It in other words is very reactive. (I can never do an easy paper properly).

Sorry, I have a tereble headache. Please forgive me.

Dear examiner I have never come across this symble ΔH before during my work so naturally it is a guess that I have made.

I guessed lithium oxide on the basis of revision.

It was deduced that the relative atomic masses of hydrogen and oxygen were such because the calculation couldn't of been done without such a deduction.

1 amp 1 gram 50 mins | This is physics |

A Further Education College student wrote this: first in pencil, and then – very neatly – in ink.

CHEMISTRY

The hours of chemistry rapidly pass away
While friends sit happily and chat.
True, we have to carry out the experiment for the day
But there is still time for that.

'Time?' the teacher roars at us
'Don't you realize that is what we're lacking?
To learn all chemistry in a one-year course
Is as difficult as receiving a huge big whacking.'

Nevertheless, unmoved, we try to achieve our goal
That is, our chemistry in one year passing.
We work all day, never resting our weary souls,
Until finally we are near to collapsing.

The examination day is near,
And again we can be found lost in study.
But paper One has much to fear,
And our future path seems very muddy.

So, having taken and failed our Paper One
We suddenly see the light,
What we thought was true, it can't be done
Never mind, paper two will be all right

'Who said that?' asks my chattering pal
As we quietly slip out of the exam,
Paper Two was as hard as hell,
So we talk of our holidays in Durham.

I agree, but I don't really mind,
At least I have written some poetry.
I hope it will be a change for you
From reading boring essays on chemistry.

Ain't the faintest idea, I must have been asleep when they done that.

The reason parts of the above diagram are drawn in pen is that is that the point of my pencil broke while drawing the card cover. *Later in script...* Borrowed pencil from invigilator.

After deep (and irrelevant) mathematical treatment of the mass spectrometer.
This isn't much good for chemistry but I don't stand much of a chance of passing anyway so I did it because I enjoy it.

End of Script
I feel at this point I must apologise to the examiner for subjecting him or her to reading this drivel. I give no excuse apart from the fact that I don't understand chemistry.

That's it, sorry but I could never do chemistry well.

I would have continued with this nice question but due to time factor I am afraid I am just about to stop writing. Hope you would not penalize me for so.

['... Hence, using these data, calculate the relative atomic mass of tin, showing clearly how the answer is obtained'.]
You can find the relative atomic mass of tin by looking at the periodic table. In the top right hand corner of every little box there is a number. This is the Relative Atomic Mass.

A diamond structure is too difficult for me to draw but I do know what it looks like. (Do I get an extra mark?)

Dear Examiner,
I know exactly what you must be thinking now - 'My God, what an idiot this child must be'. My chemistry is bad, but it usually isn't as bad as this, but during the exam I kept sneezing due to hayfever, and the medication which I took before hand nearly sent me to sleep. I'm very sorry that you have had to waste your time marking my paper!!!!!

dear examiner sorry but not enough time
[This candidate achieved 9%]

End of script in June
See you in November! Nicht bin sehr gut ist da? Nein das ist so.

(I'm sorry can't think any thing only five minutes to go)

Here endeth my exam.

Words, Words, Words...

Nitrogen in the air is more purer and when collected out of the air the unwanted gases are easily exterminated.

The reason the reaction was so slow was that the reaction was not very rapid.

This addition reaction occurs when the reactants are reacted under luminous light.

An unsaturated hydrocarbon is one which could contain more molecules than it does do already.

Bauxite is found in Guano.

The proportion of air is fairly constant as many plants exhume oxygen all the time.

Preparation of chlorine
The main impurity in the gas is carbon, this can be removed by flirtation.

Oxygen could be obtained from liquid air by diffraction.

A piece of white phosphorus was affixed on the end of a length of
wire and invested up into a granulated glass tube.

> **Hydrogen chloride is the main inpuritie and can be removed by
> passing water.**

'What is meant by sublimation?'

Solid $\overset{\text{heat}}{\longrightarrow}$ gas vapour: liquid stage is unsurpassed.

> **Sublimation is when a solid changes to a liquid or a liquid
> changes to a solid without becoming a gas.**

When water is added to the ethanoic acid an exogenic reaction
takes place the hydrogen in the water makes the acid more concentrated and so have a more effective effect on blue litmus paper.

> **Oxidation is the loss of hydrogen caused by the gain of hydrogen.**

When the mixture is cooled goblets of lead appear in the bottom of
the furnace.

> **The brine is mixed in the mercury/sodium anagram the electrode
> deposit the sodium hydroxide from the sodium chloride soln.**

The reactivity of oxygen with nitrogen and phosphorus are almost
the same because they are below each other in the electrochemical
series.

> **It must be noted that the melting point of a substance is the
> temperature at which it melts.**

Saturated hydrocarbons are those who in the terms of the leyman
cannot take on another hydrogen.

> **The term 'addition reaction' refers to a substance that induces
> additional reactions that are not needed.**

In Graphite the molecules of carbon are placed hexangonaly in
layers. The carbon molecules of quite far apart making graphite a
soft material. In diamond the molecules aplaced ochetreaheadily
and very close together making a very hard form.

> **When potassium bromide is added to silver nitrate and allowed
> to stand in sunlight the liquid slowly went clear. The reaction is
> chromatography.**

Aqueous potassium bromide is added to aqueous silver nitrate and the mixture is allowed to stand in sunlight for some hours the solution would turn a paler colour. It is called choreography.

This diagram shows how the salt are formed into stagmites and stagagmites by the rainwater dissolving the limestone and leaving small deposits of the salt behind.

Graphite is bonded with only 4 atoms. One of the electrons is not joined together. These are deionised electrons.

When powdered manganese(IV) oxide is added to an aqueous solution of hydrogen peroxide, blubbles of oxgen are produced.

The manganese(IV) oxide acts as a catalyst and is left behind unchemically changed.

'Metre tube' diffusion experiment

$$\text{Velocity} = \frac{\text{atomic weight of ammonia}}{2}$$

The soap combines with the mineral causeing it to make the soap flake.

Addition reaction is one that occurs before the actual reaction is required or expected.

Water has almost no effect on copper. A slight green coating may be formed but it doesn't affect the constituency of the water. Copper is a hard worthy metal and doesn't conduct electricity fast.

Pass the water through a tower of iron exchange resines (e.g. zealots).

A saturated hydrocarbon is a hydrocarbon which contains more hydrogen atoms than carbon atoms or vice verse.

An addition reaction is a reaction that takes place where a substance gain something from nothing instead of just changing its original structure.

(i) a saturated hydrocarbon is one that can hold as much liquid a substance as it can. (ii) an unsaturated hydrocarbon is one that does not hold as much as it can.

Nitrogen is obtained by frictional distillation of air.

In order to fasten the reaction it was kept at a temperature of 30°C.

'Explain the meaning of the expression $\Delta H = -92$ kJ'

$\Delta H = -92$ kJ means that the temperature of hydrogen in this experiment is -92 kilo joules.

The weight of hydrogen is equal to -92 kilo joules.

The meaning of the expression $\Delta H = -92$ kj is that the weight of H is kJ $= -92$ g.

$\Delta H = -92$ kJ This is the amount of hydrogen needed to produce the amount of ammonia gas.

92 kilo-jewels of heat are therefore lost.

Grass is crushed in a mortar and pedstal.

The example of grass is crushed in a motor and pestle the liquid deceived is tested against the pH table.

Chemical equilibrium is when a reaction can keep on going even in a vacume because it keeps reversing itself.

In electrolysis circuit 'Altometer'

Also 'Anemometer'

Iron contains many impurities such as arson.

> Chemical equilibrium means that the pressure equals the concentration and they both equal the temperature.

Test for oxygen
It can relight a growing split.

> The gas which is discharged is the one with the lowest letter in the alphabet.

If you add water to the resulting solid you derive calcium hydroxide same what like the first reaction.

> Allotropy means that it can act as both a proton donor and a proton receiver.

Meaning of symbol $\rightleftharpoons$
This means that heat is given off in one direction and absorbed in the other.

'What information is given by $\Delta H = -197$ kJ?'

> $\Delta H = -197$ kJ means that the reaction needs only a little hydrogen in it.

> 197 killer joules of energy are taken in.

> It means that the freezing point of hydrogen is -197 kJ Kelvin scale.

> $= \Delta H = -197$ kJ This symbol means that it when hydrogen is frozen it gives off Kilojoules of heat.

Two names of saturated hydrocarbons are copper and zinc. Two names of unsaturated hydrocarbons are neon and kripton.

Name two natural substances which contain saturated hydrocarbons and are used as fuels'.
Dimons   granate

Aluminium doesn't know about displacement.

Nitrogen monoxide gave a brown smell.

Zinc will make water unharmful to iron.

Polmerization is the craking of large molecules into smaller ones.

Large monomers are broken down into smaller monomers thus producing bigger polomers.

Polymerization is a thing which as been ever increasingly since the advent of the hydrocarbon.

'A state of equilibrium' this is when the reaction has tired itself out and cannot continue further.

Meaning of 'state of equilibrium'
That everything is at a constant temperature that everything is perfect and properly balanced.

Once the reaction has been started, it is not necessary to heat the iron further, because the reaction exhibits spontaneous combustion.

When pH is added to OH we find alkaline and when pH is added to H_2SO_3 we find acid.

'How does zinc protect iron?'
The zin must have some sort of infinity for oxygen.

'How is the high temperature of the blast furnace maintained?'
By keeping a huge fire in the actual furnace which is then made to explode (blast) which keeps the furnace going.

Copper also unreactive happy to be on its own

Two simple tests for identifying amonia are adding calcium carbonate which turns the solution milky and the other is adding limewater which produces white lime at the top of the solution which is known as 'lime light'.

The zinz plating protects iron from corrosion even when the plating is broken because once the zinc protects the iron, no further reaction takes place, so when it is broken, no reaction takes place.

The term diffusion of gasses means the amount of space that the gas can cover before it looses its effect i.e. before hydrogen sulphide looses the smell.

It will be observed that a red glow permutates through the reactants.

Chlorine and oxygen have valencies 1 & 2 respectfully.

15 cm^3 of 10 M hydrochloric acid would be the mass of scandium.

A saturated hydrocarbon means that the carbon part of the molecule is completely swamped by the hydrogen part.

This reaction is called estrafaction and gives of a smell of pair drops.

Electrolysis of brine
The salt is used in this process to speed it up; to act as a catalyst, namely a substance which will help the two halves of the equation to react to gether better.

1 molecule of titanium occupies 24 litres at S.T.P.

Zinc oxide can be found to be an amphoteric substance by using a special apparatus which tells you if it is amphoteric or not.

Besides, zinc being the higher in the reactivity series it is a superior metal.

Diamond is an atrophy of carbon.

The reaction is catalysed by iron in the form of peas.

Sodium chloride in the modern state contains ions.

An esterification in the laboratory can be produced by placing an acid died in colour with an alkalia in a small dish, and watching them separate.

Another member of the halogen series is zargon it is another gas.

Exothermic means that the reaction is just the same substance after the reaction but has reacted back into what it started out as.

You add yeast and sugar and use a zmyne as a catalyst.

The name given to this family in the Periodic table is Halogens or in organic chemistry Haloganous series.

Oxygen is taken into the body, where it is used for energy and many other activities. When in the body, a burning process takes place and a residue, carbon, is left. This combines with oxygen and is exhaled as carbon dioxide.

This was a typical observation—deduction question
The green powder is chlorine (b) The gas is hydrogen as it gives out a glowing splint. The oily drops were drops of fat. (c) The aqueous solution must have been zinc.

The copper will deposed on the side and the sulphate will oxide the iron and addventuly the vessel will calaps.

B is nitrous oxide on heating it disslocated to give oxygen.

If the aluminium was not pure then the so called pure aluminium would not be pure.

The oxides of nitrogen are further mixed with ogyden to produce NO_2 and absobed in a abortion tower.

To prepare a solution if potassium nitrate that is saturated at room temperature you first of all get some potassium and heat it in an atmosphere of nitrogen to salivate it you then add water.

Steel is more refined than iron.

Pig iron is a coarse imitation of iron

Steel is difficult to use due to its malgubility.

Iodine is a sublime substance.

'*Name the family of elements of which chlorine and bromine are members.*'
Hidgons

The term exothermic means that the gas will mix with the liquid without any help.

This family of elements is nown as allotropes.

This provides evidence that the minute particles (molecules) of a gas are in a constant erotic motion. This is called Brownian motion.

Conditions under which chlorine and bromine react with hydrogen
They both play infinity to hydrogen.

An electrolyte is added to aid the arc. I believe this is alluvia.

Manganese dioxide is a oxagent.

Avagadro's Law of Simple Relations.

A prometer is a catalyst which catalizes a catalyst.

By increasing the temperature the tranquility of the molecules in equilibrium will be upset.

Diffusion gives us evidence to show how gas is very excitable.

Caption to diagram
Dramatisation of sodium chloride in fussed state.

A state of equilibrium is when one or two things are equal to one thing.

The molecules would want to diffuse expandingly.

Thermal decomposition – decomposes heat.

The name given to the series of saturated hydrocarbons of formula C_nH_{2n+2} is the electro-chemical series.

This series is called *Oganic* chemistry (Natural occurrences).

A saturated hydrocarbon that has absorbed water to the point where no more can be absorbed. An unsaturated hydrocarbon is a hydrocarbon that has had all water driven off.

> Saturated hydrocarbon is when water is added to the substance to the point when it can no longer take any more.

O_3 has a great infinity for water and the reaction of the disolving it in water would be quite figurous.

> Ethene is converted into polythene by isomerism.

Saturated hydrocarbon is a hydrocarbon which has been saturated. A unsaturated hydrocarbon is a hydrocarbon which hasn't been saturated.

> Saturated carbons are ones which have a high quantity of energy and sugar while unsaturated hydrocarbons are ones which have their sugar and energy reduced by chemical reactions.

Polythene – a very voluble plastic.

The untra violate rays cause a chemical change in the couloring.

> Chlorine water loses its colour when it is exposed to sunlight due to a process of photosynthesis, the sunlight adsorbs the colour from the chlorine water.

State Avogadro's Law
It states that equal volumes of equal atoms they must have equal molecules.

Calcium hydrogen carbonate is picked up by mountain stream: as it passes over certain types of soil and rock the sedentary i: picked up in the water in the forms of ions.

This is Boyle's Law that the total weight of gas is inversley proportional to its own weight.

Allotropy is the study of allotropes.

Tested with a burning splint, hydrogen will distinguish the flame.

The law is the law is the law of constant composition.

All the moles in hydrochloric acid are used and know where they are travelling to.

A fowl smelling gas is given off, this being ammonia

Magnesium (the only metal that burns is CO_2) burns because it is very flourscent.

A mixture is the combination of two different elements forming : compound while a compound which has two different substan ces in it forms together and stays until reacted to form a mixtur of compounds.

Exothermic' means the reaction takes place outside.

The reaction which takes place are that the cathode is being attracted to the anode by an electric current. This is known as Electrovalency.

Diffusion of a gas is the gas which explodes. Fire causes a gas to diffuse.

Bromine is a red hot liquid.

Diffusion is the intermangling which occurs between the molecules of gases.

Why does aluminium not react with steam until red heat?' The aluminium has physical strength and needs the push to get over the hump.

The positive ions are negatively charged and vice versa.

At the cathode and the anode the same thing happens at both but in reverse.

An ion is an electrically charged participle.

Calcium has two electrons in its third shell and losses these to assume the falsification of a noble gas.

Polymerisation is the combination of discreet molecules into a collective molecules.

It appears in a group in which all the constituents have one electron in their outer 'shell' known as Halogens, also it is a diabetic gas.

Gay Lussac's Law: Equal volumes of all gases, are inversely proportional to its pressure as long as the temperature is kept constant.

Gay Lussac's Law: If a gas is an equilibrium it will oppose any force opposing it.

Photosynthesis is the word used for the pictures taken of a reaction of a mixture. The pictures are taken at different stages of the reaction. The picture shows how the substances react on their own.

Ironically oxidation is election loss.

23

∴ NaOH has morality of 1.

A piece of sodium (pea size) is placed on a deflating spoon.

Avagardo's Law. What goes up must come down.

Lithium metal would be extracted from Lithium Chloride by hydronification. It would be extracted in this way because chlorine has effinity for hydrogen.

Amphoteric oxide mean's that the oxide in the air (ampher).

Amphoteric oxide is one that glows in the dark

Aluminium is a self galvanising element and it protects itself.

[*Name of monomer*]   Monothene
[*Name of corresponding polymer*]   Polythene

Water: or The Final Solution
(with Air, Hydrogen, and Oxygen)

Water, Water, everywhere
Nor any stop to think.

> Samuel Taylor Coleridge, *The Rime of the Ancient Mariner*
> (adapted).

The water in a bath is best removed by the addition of sodium carbonate.

The most suitable way to remove harness of water from a bath is to add caustic soda.

The most suitable method to removed the hard water supply in a house is by changing the pipes.

Removal of 'fur' from kettle

This can be removed from the kettle by emense heating of the metal. This causing the metal to melt. Then you drag of the (slag) the impurities (i.e. the chemicals causing the hardness).

Hardness of water means that in serten types of water there are diffrent hardness. These are 1, Permanat hard found in chalky growend 2, Tempery hard found in clay growend, and 3 soft found in granit growend.

'Why is liquid hydrogen peroxide used with rocket fuels?'
This will react and liberate oxygen which will help the men inside the rocket to breath more freely.

Liquid hydrogen peroxide is used in rocket fuels, to give a bigger reaction and to keep the fuel tank clean inside.

Hydrogen peroxide is used in rocket fuels because it helps to burn efficiently and also prevents 'knocking' in the engines.

Action of rain water on limestone
After many years either a cave is formed or the structure capsizes.

When calcium is added to water an eruption takes place and screen's have to be used to stop the bites flying everywhere.

Hydrogen is used on a large scale in the Blast Furnace.

Hydrogen is used in fire extinguishers.

Hydrogen is used on a large scale for filling hot air balloons.

Hydrogen is used universally for hydro-electric power.

Hydrogen is used for filling up tyres.

Hydrogen is used as an anaesthetic in hospital.

Hard water is particularly beneficial for atomic reactors etc. Du
ing the war Germany set up large hard water plants in order t
make a particular kind of explosive.

Beneficial effect of hard water
It is good for teeth and bones resulting in a healthier body when
drunk.

The soap molecule is like a big tadpole. The head is attached t
the dirt etc, and the tail to the water. When the plug is pulled, i
the bath etc, the tail end of the soap drags the dirt down the drai

The water supply to the house can have flurine put in it to stop the
hardness, also it can be heated so that the calcium carbonate is
reduced to calcium oxide.

The water in a bath can be removed by the Permutit process c
more easily by the addition of ammonia.

ur is formed when you boil a kettle because the impurities cool aster than the water.

The best way of getting rid of hard water in a bath is to pour onto it a lot of soapy water. To get rid of the hard water from the supply to a home. Would be best to boil the water in a big boiler kind of tub.

Hardness in water is caused by impurities such as calcium and magnesium which are present in the rain.

'Explain the term 'hardness of water'. What causes (i) temporary hardness, (ii) permanent hardness?'
It hurts to have a shower or not. (i) carbonates (ii) illiterates

Chemical compounds which form permanent hardness in water are slaked lime and flourine. Limestone comes from the ground and on heating becomes slaked lime. Flourine is put into our water by Local Health Authorities.

Hard water is when there is not enough hydrogen present in the molecular structure of water.

To remove the temporary hardness from water in a bath, the water should be boiled.

Water in a bath is on a far more domestic scale and can be got rid of by adding a soap or detergent solution, forming a scum which can be treated equally as effectively.

27

The closer to the sea the water is the more harder it may get because there are more chalk cliffs near the seas edge than in land.

Hardness of water all increases the surface tension so that soap and detergents are able to penitrate it less easily.

The hardness of water in a bath can be removed by either boiling the water or running the water only from the hot tap and leaving it to cool instead of adding cold water.

The fur in a kettle can be removed by using an acid. The one mos commonly used is formic acid. This is obtained from ants.

The hardness of water in a bath can be removed by adding soup to the bath (especially soup eg. de 'comp' from Chanel's gordan)
[That's what after painstaking study I decided he had written...]

The organic compound of soap does not react with compounds e hard water and this has also been illustrated in University o Oxford.

Hard water forms an insoluble scrum with soap because its content caustic acid which will not mix with soap.

Cause of hard water
The water rushing through hitting rocks or other objects cause small reaction to take place.

The soap when added to water lessens surface tension which joins particles in the water together, which collects at the top.

28

Water gradually becomes heavier therefore after some days it would eventually mix with the copper(II) sulphate. It would take a few days for the water to become heavier.

you used Pottasasum water pipes it would react violently to roduce hydrogen, therefore copper is used.

The most suitable way to remove the hardness in the water for a house is to pass a small electric current threw the water.

o distinguish a gas jar of hydrogen from carbon dioxide you could olour the gas before it was placed inside the jar. If the hydrogen vas coloured, you would observe that the colouring would go traight to the top of the gas jar because hydrogen is lighter than air, nd it would diffuse from the top downwards.

The calcium could have got into the rivers and lakes by the death of small animals.

he main impurities in sea water is salt and sand. The salt can be ot rid of by boiling the water. The sand which is silicon dioxide an be got rid of by adding calcium carbonate.

To obtain pure water from sea water
Filteration e.g. leave the water to settle the salt will fall to th
bottom. This method is very slow for modern day use.

The atmosphere contains silicon which reacts like this:

$$PbCO_3 + (Si \rightarrow PbOSI + O_2$$

The sea water is boiled to a certain temperature until the salt
evaporated, and a solution of water void of the salt is left.

When water is added to the limestone the limestone absorbs the
water and it becomes hard again. When it is heated it becomes soft.

Because when sun shines on the limestone for a long time
produces a hole in the limestone.

The water in rivers and streams in limestone are is liable to be hard
water because when melted lime stone falls in the water it hardens
the water. To soften the water you must filter it and then heat it.

'Name the two main gases dissolved in tap water and state the
source'
Hydrogen and carbon dioxide. They come from fish etc.

$\Delta H = -197$ kJ is the point or temperature at which the hydrogen
becomes a liquid.

The caves are formed because after some time (aeons of time) th
limestone (calcium carbonate) decomposed giving off a gas leav
ing spaces which become caves.

The water in these areas is very hard. With limestone being a soft
rock the hard water can erode the rocks fairly easily forming caves.

Many caves are found in limestone areas because that is when
most of the chalk comes from. The limestone areas are very cha
ky with boulders of chalk and clay.

The water from rivers and springs in limestone areas are liable to be
hard water because when stalagmites and stalagtites form in the
caves the calcium carbonate falls in the rivers and springs. The rain
water shapes the mites and tites and the remaining of the limestone
flows in the springs making the water hard.

Many caves are formed in the limestone area as when the rai
falls the rain reacts with the limestone and melts it so formin
caves and gouges.

think nitrogen is produced when the inert gasses are made to react when the temperature is 1000°C+ during a lightning storm maybe.

Because the limestone is gradually reduced by heat from the sun and finally breaks down to form a powder and carbon dioxide gas evolved. Thus holes begin to appear due to this decomposition.

Many caves formed in limestone areas because the limestone is very soft compound, and when any slight movement made layers and layers of the limestone will fall making caves.

There are some many caves formed in limestone areas because the limestone crystallizes into quartz.

When coke or charcoal is burned in an open fire a light blue flame is often seen on the surface of the fire. This is hydrogen from the air burning. The hydrogen is taken from the air, usually from the moisture in the air.

The reason why many caves are formed in limestone areas is because the water is stronger than the limestone so eats its way through the limestone leaving holes (caves).

There are many caves found in limestone areas as this is a scum which solidifes and builds up with the addition of acid from the rain plus rock to make the caves.

Oxygen is respired by the plants to create equilibrium and to make up for the loss due to excessive exust fumes (carbon monoxide). Hydrogen is derived from the rotting vedgetation and fish in the water.

Many caves are formed in limestone areas because it is a white lumpy solid.

The hydrogen chloride in water acts as a strong acid because it is being dissolved for the first time and is carrying a lot of electrons while the acetic acid has been dissolved before and only has few electrons.

Hydrogen is a dangerous gas if left to its own devices.

Limestone on its own is a stable compound with a very low rate of combustion.

Hydrogen can be tested by a lighted flint. If whole, it will burn quietly; if not, there will be a small squeak.

The cloudy liquid is limestone.

Reason for constant proportion of oxygen in air
Because too much oxygen invigorates the organism and it becomes over-active. So only small quantities of oxygen are used by every living creature and the proportion stays constant this way.

32

When at night more people are stationary and thus using less oxygen the plants reverse their cycle to give out carbon dioxide and so keeps this 28% fairly constant.

Plants 'breath' in CO_2 and 'breath' out O_2 thus keeping the O_2 breathing animals suppressed.

Oxygen has a high boiling point of 100 °C.

Water is a compound of hydrogen and oxygen because when heated it is dehydrated and gives of hydrogen peroxide.

Fish are able to breathe in stagnant water utilizing the oxygen in the water and releasing hydrogen.

Water is a compound of hydrogen and oxygen because there is enough oxygen in the sea to keep sea creatures alive.

Pieces of evidence which support the view that water is a compound of hydrogen and oxygen is that

(1) Water is passed in the blast furnace as steam and the hydrogen and oxygen is separated to make the carbon monoxide carbon dioxide and the hydrogen going with the limestone.

(2) If water is added to anhydrous copper sulphate the colour changes to blue. This is because oxygen from the water has turned the copper into copper oxide and the hydrogen is given off as a gas.

The hydrogen peroxide decomposes into water ($HO_5 \rightarrow H_2O$) and somtimes heavy water (H_2O_2)

It is possable to use liquid air to obtain oxygen as it is of a specific gravety compared to all the other air gases. As the air turn to liquid each liquid floats at a certain point because of the density of the liquid and so the oxegen may be drawn off.

The hydrogen gases is tested by a poping blazing splint.

Pure water must contain hydrogen because oxygen would float away if it was not for hydrogen.

CO is a light gas, because of the proportions and its relation to oxygen. Both oxygen and carbon are light gases therefore they are air borne.

The meaning of 'hydrogen' is that it contains oxygen.

Hydrogen: Used to be in airships, now used for blast furnaces, gas stoves, and blacksmiths; in the air that we breathe.

Two manufacturing process in which hydrogen is used on a large scale
Blown up footballs etc.
At the dentist

Hydrogen is used in the hydrogen bomb, where Hydrogen diffuses with the air causing an explosion.

Oxygen is also used in fire extinguishers.

If water is evaporated off long enough the hydrogen and oxygen will part when this happens the oxygen will sink lower than the hydrogen in a gas jar.

Water needs oxegen other wise it is not water because without oxegen hydrogen would just be by itself.

Put a lighting stick in hydrogen it will explood with a squekey pop, meaning hydrogen.

Heat the pure water and collect the steam in a jar. Light a splint and immerse in the steam if the split 'pops' – Hydrogen is present.

Rain water is put in container for dissillation. The water is heated and since hydrogen is the lightest gas, it will diffuse into the atmosphere leaving the water left to distill into a container. The water contains mostly oxygen.

Hydrogen is used to make explotions.

Hydrogen used for manufacturing amonia and weather balloons.

One common large scale use of hydrogen is in the atomic or hydrogen bomb, although only two of these bombs have ever been used the need for hydrogen for this purpose is great.

Water is an oxide of hydrogen becos its formaley shos that.

Hydrogen is used for fire extinguishers as it will not burn. It is used also by many firm to produce the fizz in pop. It also helps in making bread rise and cakes.

Obtain an amount of hydrogen and air sealed in separate gas jars, open the gas jars simultaneously and watch the gas to see which one diffuses first.

Hydrogen is place in a porpus pot. (It is known that hydrogen can diffuse through porpus).

A balloon filled with hydrogen and another this time filled with air are fixed to the ground. At a given signal they are both freed at the same time. The bottoms of the balloons are not tied therefore once they are set free the gas is free to come out. The hydrogen in the hydrogen-filled balloon comes back to the ground first. This shows that the hydrogen has diffused faster than the air, hence emptying the balloon and causing it to fall.

When a crystal of potassium permanganate is dropped into a beaker of water the vapour will gradually diffuse upwards until it has entirely swamped the water with its purple color.

When the water has finished raising the reading should be taken and by mathematics the Percentage of Oxygen can be worked out.

dehydration of an alcohol this is when alcohol has been changed from 1 condition to another and it changes the condition of its surroundings e.g. when a person drinks too much the alcohol changes from a liquid to a gas the alcohol absorbs into the blood and it harms the drinker.

[*Finally - I wouldn't have believed it possible, but...*]
The formula of water could be: 00.80

Structure: or, How It Hangs Together

Search, dismayed, the dark profound
Where nature works in secret; trace the forms
Of atoms, moving with incessant change
Their elemental round...

> Mark Akenside (adapted for the motto of *The Chemist*, 1824–5, and further adapted).

Structure of sodium chloride
Each ion is connected to another ion in six difference dimensions.

The bonds between a graphite molecule are weak Waff de graph bonds.

Aluminium is used in cooking foil as it prevents radiation due to its close nit molecular structure.

The graphite has cathederal or diamond like crystaline structure.

Astatine will be much less reactive than the other halogens as that is what the use of the periodic table entails.

The graphite is very flaky and slippery but that does not affect its chemical properties as compared to diamonds. Because it is what they are composed of is really what they are, and not what they look like.

Diamond is hard because of its structure, graphite is soft because of the same thing.

Iron is a grey metal which high density because it is heavy in lifting it. It conducts electricity because it is a good conductor of electricity.

'Why is diamond hard and graphite flaky and slippery?'
This is because diamond is usually found near volcanos where the larva errupts and diamond is made great het is evolved in making diamond while could be made of wood which when burnt gives a black colour and that is graphite. While diamond is not exactly seen just like it is found in some kind of a shell.

The electrons in the iron is free to move and the electrons in the sulphur is holding each other firmly and not easy to mobile. The mass of iron is greater than the sulphur so the density of the iron is also greater.

Iron is able to conduct electricity because it forms electrocovalent bonds. Therefore there are more free electrons to charge. Sulphur however has covalent attractions and is not subverse to electrical conductivity.

Sulphur is non-magnetic and will not carry electrical currant waves where as iron is magnetic and so the eletric current can flow through the iron bar due to all the magnetic particles running in one direction by the domain theory from north to south.

Graphite's structure is such that it is not so riged and made up in layers with weeker bonds holding each layer (van der wahol forces) i.e. if a little force is aplide to graphite the bond holding the layer brackes.

Iron conducts electricity more easily because it stays a solid when heated in which the electrons gain extra power on colliding with each other and thereby setting off a chain reaction.

In graphite the atoms are arranged in their shapes differently than the other allotrope the atom is ionised therefore reduction has taken place whist the other compound has been oxidised.

Graphite has holes in the structure, diamond is closely packed together and therefore no flors for it to crumble. As diamond is flatter than graphite it also has a different colour and lasts longer.

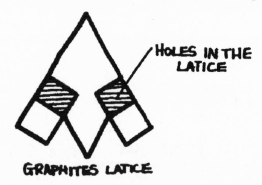

HOLES IN THE LATICE

GRAPHITES LATICE

In a dimond there is a sea of electrons that is the electrons are so closely packed that they appear as a mass or sea of electrons.

Silica is much weaker as a glass because all the tension is concentrated on the bonds and if an alkali attacks one bond then the tension will concentrate on that bond while the alkali attacks the other bonds and breaks them.

Dimonds go round in fours but graphite molecules go round in threes.

Allotropes are organic compounds. The allotropes of carbon are layer upon layer of atoms sliding on top of one another. Gold is an other form of allotropes which is an organic compound occurs naturally and its molecular structure is very complicated.

> **The bonds in the carbon dioxide are breaking and forming at an incredible rate so as to leave the carbon dioxide in gas form.**

Steel is not made up of as many atoms they have more room to move about and this makes steel much more piable than iron.

> **When calcium is placed in the water it is still for a few seconds because the water has to get to the inside of the atom. As they go down the scale the atoms become larger and therefore it takes longer.**

The HCl molecules burst open by letting the water molecules enter their molecules the pressure inside the HCl molecule that it burst.

> **The molecules of gas when taken out from under pressure spread out. This makes them rather small thus be able to pass through small spaces.**

If the temperature of the gas was increased the electrons would become excited and would rush about at fantastic speeds increasing the diffusion of the gas in all directions.

> *Bonding in methane*
> **There are 26 protons 26 neutrons in the nucleus of the methene atom It has 26 electrons in its outer shell.**

'Why do crystals of sodium chloride have a regular shape?'
Crystals of sodium chloride have a regular shape. Because sodium chloride is a salt. Crystals of salts have a regular shape therefor it is true.

> **Diamond is an allotrope of carbon. If the melting point of diamond was extremely low then it would melt so easy.**

The melting point of diomond is extreamly high as it is a very ridged structure that has to be brocken down.

> **Chlorine has 7 electrons in her outer shell so she forms an ion with a negative charge.**

Solid sodium does this as it has very large molecules in it and the electricity can easily pass in between the molecules. Sodium chloride is a non-conductor because the chlorine when cold has got very small molecules so they fit in between the sodium molecules, so blocking the gaps for the electricity to get through.

Sodium chloride acts as a semi-conductor i.e. germanium.

The elements of this family show the same similarities because they are in the same column of the periodic table which tells us that these are made in the same era as the members are.

When sodium chloride is is a alkidine therefor a non-conductor chlorine present is greater than sodium when solid – but when melted the sodium becames an electric conductor the chlorine is evaporated only leaving the conductoress sodium present.

Nitric acid is a proton remover. Protons are negatively chaged and so leaves an excess of positively charged electrons.

Graphite lattice is built up upon a cube structure, wereas the sulphur lattice, is built up upon a sliding scale, creating less friction, when the melt is heated.

If excess Zn was added the Zn would finally expire all its charge on to one atom of Zn, the rest would be come neutrally charged and only one atom would become supercharged.

A gas would change its rate if the temperature was increased. It would move much faster as the molecules bump into the waves of heat and then bounce of and on to each other.

Evidence which diffusion provides concerning nature of gases
The evidence which are concerned with the natures of gases, with be the hydrocarbon gase such as methane and ether because these are the alkanes compound or the properties, which when forming of the double bond. The rate of diffusion of a gas to change would take place when the rate of reaction of the exothermic and endothermic follows it change the temperature of the gas. When the reaction is exothermic it increase is temperature and when the process of endothermic take place the temperature of the gas decrease to it certain level, and on the other hand they could be measured by the Gas Equation following the Boyle's Law.

In flurine there are 10 nutrons in the nuceous.

In the nucleus there are 10 neutrons and 9 proteins.

Diamond is the graphite of carbon.

The Sodium ionic structure isn't so fridgid.

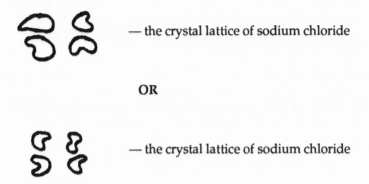

— the crystal lattice of sodium chloride

OR

— the crystal lattice of sodium chloride

'How does its crystal structure account for the high melting point of sodium chloride?'
The high melting point of sodium chloride is too high.

The particles present in the crystal lattices of sodium are acidic nutrients.

Sodium is Na therefore its structure is made up of Nitrogen and ammonia.

Sodium in a solid state is a good conductor of electricity because in this state the sodium contains water which conducts electricity.

Carbon dioxide has no melting point as it is not a solid at standard temperature and pressure.

The electrons are swaped backward and farward very quckly so quickly infact that it is hardly noticable at all.

A covalent bond is a bond which has split electrons which share an atom.

Atomic arrangement in diamond and graphite

They are arranged in crystal-formation. You can tell how tightly they are packed, how excited they might be and how fast they move. The atoms in graphite are excited. This proves the substance to be radioactive, as graphite emits radiation.

> **One atom which needs four more atoms to look like one of the inert gases looks for somebody else who needs four more electrons to make its shell full and look inert they therefore decide to come to gether and share each others electrons and form a molecule.**

A neutron has a mass of -1.

> **In Diamond the atoms are arranged octredral. In Graphite the atoms are arranged Hexagonadral.**

An electrovalent bond is a force which transfer atoms of a molecule to complete the outer orbit which travels round the nucleus.

> **An electrovalent bond is that bond which hold together elements by electromotive forces.**

The electrons fly around the nucleus on two shells.

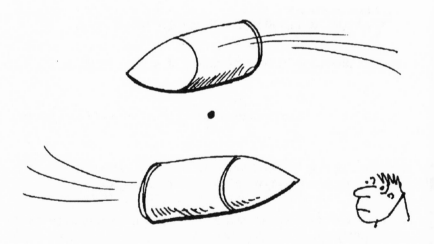

> **Chlorine has 17 electrons and that gives him a 2,8,7 configuration, he is unstable**

e.g. The transition metals seem to be all in the same period of the table e.g. copper nickel etc. The rare gases seem to be in the same period. We don't know why they are like it but it is easier.

In the other hands, the chlorides combinate with non-metal. The bond is colvent bond. They are only by sharing electron. The bond joined the atom of the compound is weak. It is just a vast de weak force. The atom have a greater tendency to run away so it is usually a volatile liquids or gases.

Whereas iodine needs two electrons and is therefore not as chlorine. As its 'p' shell is filled it takes on an heir of stability.

[*Type of bonding*]   'Convalescent'

Industry, Commerce, and Agriculture:
or, The Answer To Economic Ills

If you have great talents, industry will improve them:
if you have but moderate abilities, industry will expose their deficiency.

Sir Joshua Reynolds, *Discourse to Students of the Royal Academy*,
11 December 1769 (adapted).

Aluminium is also used for making objects as light as possible e.g.
rockets for space and other household objects.

**Another known ester is goat sweat which is known to cause
havoc among bees.**

The aluminium also keeps the electricity safe because it does not let
the water in at the electricity anywhere.

**Lord Leverhulme port sunlight works imports sawyer bean seed
palm oil etc. This is the manufacture of soap.**

Air is taken down to a temperature of $-900\,^{\circ}$C at which air becomes
a liquid.

Ammonium phosphat is a useful fertilizer because with the combination of water it breakdowns and combines with the soil to give useful vitamins to the plants which they need to grow and bare nice fruit due to the vitamins.

Ammonium phosphate $(NH_4)_3PO_4$ is a particularly useful fertilizer because it has all the required substances which make it a good fertilizer. Above all it gives out heat in the soil and keeps it free from germs.

The nitrogen collected from the air is of no use to plants while that chemically prepared is.

It can be shown that ammonia contains hydrogen molecules and nitrogen molecules by reversing the Haber process. Pass the amonia through a depressurizing chamber.

Ammonium phosphate is used because it matures the soil giving a bit of life.

The sodium hydroxide forms an amalgum with, liquid mercury, to separate the two, heat is used, the disperited water containing sodium chloride is pumped away. The mercury is passed back through the cell and the sodium hydroxide forms pelets, because of dehydration.

A soap is and ester with an excess of acid. As in soap powder.

Aluminium is used in manufacture of aluminium window panes.

Aluminium is used in air craft as it is a very light metal, it is able to be supported by air, otherwise if it was a heavy metal it would fall to the ground.

Soap is formed from the sum when NaCl + something is boiled for 10 mins.

Copper is used for water pipes because it doesn't react with hot or cold water only steam, and the hot water only turns to steam when it leaves the pipe.

Aluminium is more resistant than iron because it is higher in the activity series and can withstand more things in the atmosphere because most of what is in the atmosphere, is again lower. That is why it can be used for aeroplanes, apart from being light and cheap.

Limestone, chalk, etc. evolved from dead plants years ago.

Name of the catalyst used in Haber process is Red lead Pelatinum.

The Haber process is carried out at a pressure of 200 Atmospheres because hydrogen is lighter than air.

Blast furnace
The iron ore is being put through water at $1000^{\circ}C$ and then through limestone which acts as a drying agent.

The process is carried out at a pressure of about 200 atmospheres so as to be protected from interuption by the earth's atmosphere.

When the process is carried out at 200 atmospheres the equilibrium will try to lower it by going to the right and raising the temperature in the exothermic direction. This way was devised by le Charlair and will give off ammonia gas always.

Galvanising tin to the surface of iron by electrolysis or paint the surface of iron which can protect air oxidise iron, such as the hull of cars which is painted by paint.

A higher grade iron is produced which can withstand the torments of industry.

How to obtain pure water from sea water
Filter using filter beds in a water treatment plant. This would remove any waste materials like, shells, Driftwood (would be remove earlier), seaweed gunge.

Oxygen is manufactured on a large scale by the combustion of air.

ndustrial process using large quantities of sulphuric acid
he tar industry in making roads.

Two substances that are manufactured from calcium carbonate are the hair and fingernails of the human body.

or example, diamond and graphite, which are both allotropes of
arbon could be used in a blast furnace to make iron because this
process begins with carbon.

Natural gas contains ethane. When gas leaves the human body it is mostly methane.

*O*ne example of a polymer manufactured commercially is steel.

'What are the usual sources of raw materials used in the Contact Process for making sulphuric acid?'
ICI and the large chemical firms.

wo substances manufactured from calcium carbonate
ndigestion tablets.

Two substances manufactured from calcium carbonate are stalag-mites and stalagtites.

*O*xygen is manufactured on large scale by boiling water and col-
ecting the oxygen and hydrogen by fission.

Aluminium is a hard metal and keeps the cold out and the heat in.

Industrial application of esterification
This process is also industrially very useful, for example fats and soap are both esters, fat being an ester of methene, C_2H_6. This process is thus indeed very useful indeed as both soap, $C_{17}H_{35}COOH$ and fat are widely used throughout the world and will continue to be so. The soap is collected at the top of the vats and is made then into the bars as we receive them.

The coke is heated with the iron ore until it becomes white and this then smelt the iron.

Fractional distillation
This is the process which is carried out at the Bushmills Distillery. The clear liquid which comes off is mainly ethanol (known as poteen).

The ethene is passed over a piece of machinery known as a 'nut-cracker'.

Fractional distillation again
By heating the cruel oil in a fractional furnace.

Steel and brass are usually present in pig iron.

One iron ore would be lead.

The coke, at such a high temperature, gives off a gas (known as methane) and when all this gas is given off, what remains is iron

The iron is used to heat the mixture it is just like passing sulphur dioxide over platnium amandemium in the manufacture of sulphuric acid.

The high temperature of the blast furnace is maintained by keeping it going for twenty four hours non stop all the year round.

Quicklime can be used in the manufacture of medicines.

The cathode is a moveing river of mucury.

Sodium hydroxide is used in the manufacture of all those things cos it does the right job cheeply

Sodium hydroxide is a good conductor of electricity that's why it is also used in the manufacture of soap.

Sodium hydroxide is used in soaps as it is a harmless way of hydrating the oils so that they will not irritate the skin.

Electrolysis of brine
The cathode is a flow of platinum.

An industrial process in which a catalyst is in the production of ammonia from nitrogen and hydrogen by the Le Chattilers process were nitrogen and hydrogen are passed over burning platinum gauze. The temperature and pressure are also crucible to the test the pressure is about 400°C.

A large scale use for calcium hydroxide is for decomposing dead bodies.

In the formation of ammonia by the Harber process a catalyst is used to fasten the reaction up.

In an industrial process where oxygen is released from a weed, the catalyst used to alter the speed of the reaction is light.

Sulphuric acid is a very strong acid, it is used to remove pests etc.

Sulphuric acid can be used in the production of more sulphuric acid and also in producing rockets.

The only materials needed are sulphur, which is mined in America because of its near absolute purity, and oxygen which is come from the air.

'Why is zinc used to protect iron?'
Because zinc is uncorrosible and therefore its ideal for lead as it is used on roofs and things.

The Sulpher dioxide is obtained from Heating Iron Pirates.

Soapmaking consists of sodium hydroxide and acetic acid. Heat this solution and a strong odour begins which is the ester then the solution becomes like jelly. This how perfumed soap is made.

Fermentation. This is done in the lab from beer. Once you hav⟨ added yeast to beer it reacts & gives of gases & the flavour of th⟨ yeast goes into the beer. The temp. should be about 60° (roon temp) and the beer should be left for about 1 month.

Good quality wine has been fermented for 200 years whereas beer, the maximum is a week.

Nitric acid is used in the Haber process, and also in laundry work

Nitric acid is used as an anaestic in medecin.

Nitric acid is used in the production of soft drinks and sweets i.e⟨ flavourings and as nail polish remover.

To use this process of seperation the air must be frozen until it is liquid. Then the frozen air is put into a coloumn There it is frozen even more so the temperature reaches the certain freezing point of each commodity of air so when one commodity is frozen the others are still in a liquid state so the commodities can be separated.

Acetylene is a nail varnish remover.

The catalyst is plasters asbestoes.

> **Aluminium combin with iron forming alloy a very strong mital, avoiding rusting and has a shining face.**

mportant compounds from ammonia
'ertalizers and hospital sprits

> > *Conditions for synthesis of ammonia*
> > **If the pressure is increased the state of equilibrium will slow down.**

3ecause the ammonia gas might melt.

> > *'Why is limestone used in the blast furnace?'*
> > **Lime stone is used to remove earthly impurities.**

[ron corrodes faster than aluminium under the same atmospheric
conditions because the atoms on the surface of the aluminium are
continually fighting off the oxide film which tries to settle onto it.
Whereas iron hasn't any defence against the oxide film.

> > *Three uses of aluminium:*
> > **1) Saucepans (high melling piont)**
> > **2) Mordern artelecture (mallable)**
> > **3) Low density**

Limestone is used as a lubricant.

> **Ethanol is used widely for various purposes.**

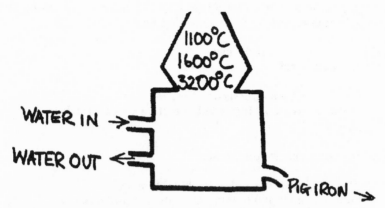

In a blast furnace there is put iron-ore and coke together they slit up and burn to a black powder after sometime you put the limestone in which changes the powder into a hard solid substances when out of the furnace they use the iron to make things.

> **Iron-ore and coke are put into a blasting furnace to blast out all the iron-ore's impurities.**

Pig iron is made whereas steel in mined.

> **One commercial use for calcium oxide is industrial use. Commercial use for calcium oxide and coke is coal.**

Fermentation is the process by which yeast is allowed to ferment in great quantities the bacteria involved is zymase which is rapidly reproducing causing the solution to become alcohol.

> **Al often used for overhead power cables because it conducts a positive (+ve) velocity.**

Aluminium is manufactured from pure aluminium oxide by an ark furness.

Hydrogen was largely used as filling gas in balloons and Zyppylins, but because of the danger of explosion, this is not done anymore.

In weilding equipment oxy-acytenle wielding.

Onether Method could be by using some type of *enzyme*. This is common method for preparing drinking alcohol i.e. meth's spirit.

Aluminium has very high infinity of electricity, there fore it is used to store high voltge of electricity.

Sulphuric acid is made commercially by using verminium as a catylist. This speeds up the reaction in the abortion tower.

Copper ore is dug out of open mines and immersed in water. The copper is then taken out of the water and the copper content in the water is brought out by immersing green wooden poles in the solution, after the copper is taken off the poles, It's burnt with oxygen to form copper oxide. The poling method is ancient and primitive but it is still the most effective.

Graphite can only be mined horizontally.

In photosynthesis nitrogen is taken from the air automatically by the leafs on plants. This nitrogen is an essentiall part of their intake as it helps in the conversion of food into sugar and glucose.

Photosynthesis is the breeding of plants and also it is the name given to the process of artificial breeding.

Photosynthesis is process which plantlife perform. Daylight, moisture and air must be present in order that the plantlife may eat.

Photosynthesis is when the plant takes in light and transforms it into chlorine which it needs for survival. The light and air go into the leaf and a chemical change takes place to form chlorine.

Photosynthesis is a prosses were by the rays from the sun act as a catalist to the reaction of cloroform and carbohydrates forming in the leaves of plants.

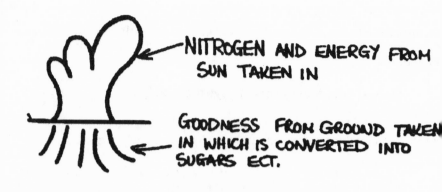

NITROGEN AND ENERGY FROM SUN TAKEN IN

GOODNESS FROM GROUND TAKEN IN WHICH IS CONVERTED INTO SUGARS ECT.

Photosynthesis is the ability in plants to change salts from the earth into clorafill by the use of sunlight it is also used for separating out different substances in a dye or coloured liquid by dropping some on a filter paper and leting it absorb up warter.

> Photosynthesis is the reaction of a substance which is used in large scale production of something to help obtain the required material.

Oxidation occurs when a free oxygen atom is made. Ozone which can be smelt whilst near the sea is an oxide and attacks iron objects. To stop this Blackpool Tower has to be painted several times a year.

> Fractional distillation – mixture of X and Y, put in a blast furnace (or bunsen).

If it wasn't for the decomposers in the soil, we would all be knee deep in urine and theses.

Experiments and Apparatus:
or, How It Works and How It's Done

In the full tide of unsuccessful experiment...

    Thomas Jefferson, *First Inaugural Address*, 4 March 1801 (adapted).

They all contain alcohol and so their reactions are similar.

The Thermite process
The aluminium snatches the oxygen away from the iron quickly
and the friction causes them to ignite.

Also see if the volts going in at the cathode were the same coming
out of the anode.

    The gas is collected in the usual way which is rarely used.

Ammonium chloride when heated will give two gases. If a piece of
litmus paper is held over the test tube half will turn blue and the
other half will turn red.

    'What is meant by the term "dehydration?"'
    If I wanted to 'dehydrate' a plum, I would heat it gently in an
oven, this would remove the water. I would be left with a disgusting dried plum.

'How are esters prepared?'
A mixture of acid and alcohol with the presence of sulphuric acid they are warmed and a fruity smell of rancid butter is present.

Potassium nitrate is purified by process called electrolysis. Slab of impure potassium are made the anode and thin sheets o potassium the cathode of a cell in which copper sulphate solutior is the electrolyte.

To form a soap you react a fat with a steroid.

$$\text{FAT} + \text{STEROID} \leftrightarrow \text{SOAP} + \text{WATER}$$

Each gas formed at the cathode is hydgreon.

The sodium chloride has its melting point lowered by strotutinum chloride hence solid sodium hydroxide is found at cathode.

Electrolysis of brine
Chlorine formed at the cathode. Helium formed at the anode.

The next four deal with the 'metre tube' diffusion experiment

A brown gas would appear at the hydrochloric acid end. (I hope)

The velocity of an abject is found either by $\dfrac{mass}{volume}$ or $\dfrac{d\,is}{time}$ or by differentiating the formulae of $acceleration = \dfrac{velocity}{t}$, velocity can be also obtained by cross multiplying acceleration x time taken. The speed of anything would increase in a vacuum a there is no gravitational force acting on it. To determine the veloc ity of this experiment I would personally record the time taken.

The cotton wool with the concentrated ammonia solution would be attracted to the cotton wool with the concentrated hydrochloric acid. The ammonia wool would move towards the wool with hydrochloric acid.

The ammonia fumes are drawn towards the hydrochloric acid faster than the ammonia can draw the hydrochloric acid fumes towards itself.

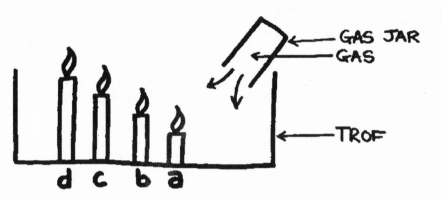

The diagram shows candles in a trof at different heights all alight. Hold the gas jar up side down and take the lid of as in the diagram. If nothing happens to the candles then the gas is hydrogen as it lighter than air, so it will quickly rise. With carbon dioxide, the flame cannot burn due to there being not oxygen, and therefore will gtinswish.

When they meet the chlorine swallows the ammonia up and then changes in a red which show that the gases are of acidic solutions.

Diffusion method for distinguishing between hydrogen and carbon dioxide
Dye the gases with a very light weight colour and watch for them to rise. The one that stays on the floor of the gas jar is carbon dioxide.

.. and again
Place both gas jar in separate small cupords, each with a candle at the bottom remove the lid of each, even though hydrogen is a light gas it will eventually diffuse equaly through the cupord and will egnight the candle. The other candle will be distinguished by the carbon dioxide.

The two gases would be forced to the opposite end of the glass tube and to do this they would have to pass through each other to reach the end of the tube.

57

To show that grass contains a mixture of coloured materials a few pieces of grass would be studied under a microscope. This is chromatography.

> Grass can be shown to have coloured materials by pouring starch over it. This takes the dyes out and one can then see the colours which were previously in the grass.

We first of all make a stain on some chromatography paper with the grass. We dip the paper in acid. We remove the paper from the acid and watch the grass particles cling to the paper and be carried up towards the top.

> Grass can be shown to contain a mixture of coloured materials by passing white lights through it to show various colours in it.

For fermentation to take place some wine, i.e. alcohol, like ethanol is bioled in a conical flask with the aid of a bunsen burner when the wine is biloing its passed through a Liegbeg condenser, which has water going in and out of it. This is how alcohol is fermentated.

> Fermentation can be carried out in the laboratory by placing some yogurt in a clonical flask and add yeast to it.

Take a blade of grass and put some ink on and observe if the ink separates out the different colours.

> I would obtain iodine from an impure sample by electrolysis of iodine. Here the electrolyte which is sulphuric acid with a little copper sulphate cleans up the or reacts with the impurities and cleaning it up or but the impure iodine in amalgar which is sodium/morcury and pass a electric current through which will transfere electrons to obtain iodine.

'Give examples of reactions of unsaturated hydrocarbons.'
Marsh gas and manure.

> Just heat the solution to drive off the water and the white powder that is left is the sodium bi-carbonate (harpic)

A glowing flint would be put into the jar.

> The percentages calculated in (iii) differ from the percentages by volume in the air because, as mentioned before, tap water has a higher gas content than normal air.

Ammonia has a great affinity for water. 1 cm^2 of ammonia absorb about 800 cm^2 of water.

The air is heated by passing it over a flame.

The dry ammonia could be collected in a gas-jar under water.

Then filter off the water of crystallisation and weight it.

Reasonably accurate method for determining the percentage volume of oxygen in air
Weight a gas jar and lid which is full of air and note the weight. Do this again and record the weight. Weigh the gas-jar again with three beakers each containing 1 cc of nitrogen, carbon dioxide and hydrogens absorbers. Re-weigh the gas jar but take out the beakers and letting in as little air as possible. An easy way to get past letting in any air is add a drop of each liquid to the bottom of the gas jar but keep them separate.

> **To distinguish between sulphuric acid and hydrochloric acid. Test. (1). Place a small amount of sulphuric acid and hydrochloric acid in a clay pot. (2). Carefully ignite these two mixtures with a tapper and allow to burn. (3). Note any changes that occur.**

Ammonium chloride smells different from sodium chloride, but goodness knows how to tell them apart using sodium hydroxide.

> *'Why is chlorine washed with a little water before collection?'*
> **To remove any impurities for example potassium. Water will adhere to the alien particles thus removing them from the chlorine leaving it pure.**

would perform this experiment inside a water bath.

I believe the white solid C to be chlorine as well as to this mainly because when ignited it goes brick red.

Chlorine is collected after it has been washed and dried by upward delivery through water.

> 'Name a suitable oxidising agent'
> **Potassium permagnet.**

The chlorine is washed to remove any stray hydrogen atoms.

> **The materials used for the electrodes are granite.**

Washing the chlorine with a little water makes the smell less strong and it becomes slightly diluted.

> **It is desirable to wash the chlorine in water because other wise the chlorine will take water from the air causing a vacuum which could crack the flask.**

The sodium hydroxid is collected by using the fountain experiment.

> *Sulphur*
> **This is a yellow soiled/liquid (i.e.gunge) that is very hydroscopic (eats water).**

It is advisable to wash the chlorine before collecting it as it may have a coating of poison collected from the atmosphere.

> **The chlorine should be washed to remove the unpleasant smell.**

I would collect the gas underwater.

Heating anhydrous sodium carbonate results in the anhydrous sodium carbonate becoming very hot.

When heated the copper(II) carbonate changes to copper(XX) carbonate.

Carbon dioxid contains carbon this can be proved by this experiment. Oxygen supports combustion and oxygen is another constituent of carbon dioxide so something stop carbon dioxide supporting combustion This must be the carbon.

$$CO_2 + flame \rightarrow extinguished\ flame$$

Take a vacuum into it place a measured amount of hydrogen and oxygen in the ratio 2:1

P = sodium chloride. This may be deduced by the brown gas, indicating chlorine, and the orange-yellow solid, indicating sodium.

Increase in pressure causes the molecules to collide more often. Increase in volume also enables the molecules to hit each other more often.

An experiment were hydrogen sulphide is a reagent in an oxidation-reduction reaction is when rust occurs on an iron bridge for example in the sea this would cause the bridge to oxidizes and reduction will occur thus producing hydrogen sulphide.

The boat will be taken away from the total and the measurement of substance before and after experiment will be taken away. The after is taken away from the before.

A labatory use of Calcium Hydroxide is as a prime example of hydroxide which has all the propterites associated with hydrox ides.

Factors which may effect the speed of chemical reactions are temperature, pressure, and time.

Iron (II) sulphide is made in the laboratory by pouring conc sulphuric acid on to iron fillings in a flask which has been tilte downwards so that water (impurity) is condensed at the neck o the flask. Iron(II) sulphide because it is denser than air i collected by downwards delivery into a gas jar.

During the reaction you would see white gas of rotten smell.

Light will also alow crystals to grow faster as they will be able t absorb the energy faster and thus grow faster.

The Thermit process is speeded up by the absorption of light.

Factors which affect reaction rates

The heating method can be seen in the electrolysis of wate where on heating the electrons or atoms get more violent an move faster and they go coliding into each other in an attempt t find a cooler spot. This speeds up the reactions.

This passing through water of the hydrogen sulphide is so that it can be dried.

Hydrogen sulphide is a wet gas and water contains hydroge (H_2O) and this makes disolving hydrogen sulphide gas difficul

Carbon dioxide could be ignited in a container.

The excess hydrogen gas passing out of the apparatus must be burnt at sauce to stop it contaminating the air in the lab.

From past knowledge I know that manganese(IV) oxide is a catalyst and when in water forms hydrogen peroxide.

A chemical test for carbon monoxide is place a tube into water and bubble carbon monoxide through it, carbon will then remain.

Carbon monoxide turns green litmus blue.

The choking gas is more than likely to be pure hydrogen.

Because when shulphuric is used there is a percinitate formed (calcium shulphate).

One gas is dyed to contrast it against the other one.

Apparatus to obtain a sample of carbon monoxide free from carbon dioxide

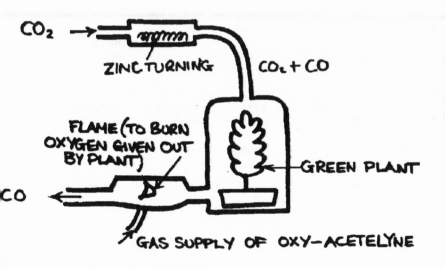

To obtain a solution containing Fe^{2+} *ions*
Heat iron(II) to get it molten form. When molten mix it with very hot water of about the same temp.

A simple experiment which shows that gases mix thoroughly
Two test tubes of known weight and volumetric capacity are each
filled with a gas which has different characteristics respectively.

Have a method of removing gasses from sight of reaction e.g. drawing off gasses with a vacume pump.

Why hydrogen peroxide should be stored in a cool, dark place
Even a drop of small blood could decompse it.

The principle impurity in the gas is downward delivery because is very soluble in water.

Bromine water loses its colour at once when ethene is added. It
used for makeing a certain sweet which is good for a sour throat

How to compare the effectiveness of manganese(IV) oxide and lead(IV)
oxide as catalysts for the decomposition of aqueous hydrogen peroxide

It would be obvious that as a catalyst manganese(IV) oxide would be more effective as a catalyst than lead(IV) oxide, the reason being is that manganese(IV) oxide is used with potassium peroxide to manufacture oxygen in a small scale so it would be logical to say that as manganese(IV) is a large contributing factor towards making oxygen with potassium peroxide, so it would be more effective as a catalyst than lead(IV) oxide as lead oxide has no part in the manufacture of oxygen.

The catylyst has speeded up the reaction so quickly that oxygen
has to slowdown because it can't bubble off quick enough.

The identify of substance x is Peardrops.

If collected over salt solution (concentrated) pear shaped ester is
seen to rise to the surface.

To obtain oxygen from the air this is done by passing it through sulphuric acid, as is known as kipp's process.

The piece of calcium metal would move across the surface of th
water like a small hovercraft. (Same principal)

'How would you collect sulphur dioxide?'
The gase is collected over a water bathe with and inverted gase jar. This is due to its being ligther than air, so the sulphur dioxid expells the water and takes its place.

Place a plant and a mouse under a bell jar. The mouse will not suffocate as long as the sun is shining, this means that the plant is producing oxygen on which the mouse can breathe directly the sun sinks the plant will stop producing oxygen and is a short while the mouse will suffocate.

o show that hydrogen diffuses faster than air

wo gas jars are filled with hydrogen and air respectively. And here is no way in which anything can get in or out. Then under pecial conditions the top is taken off so that the gas is allowed to scape. But nothing is allowed to enter and so in a vacuum would e the best suitable solution to overcome this. You would leave oth jars for a few minutes and then keeping them in a vacuum test he hydrogen with a glowing splint. Nothing happens.

ill a balloon with H_2 and let it fly and as it is denser than air it will ly towards the sky.

In the test tube you would put in some water with layer of vasalene over the top of the anhydrous water. In the third test tube you would place water with some calcium hydroxide in because this is a drying agent and it would dehydrate the water and a cork on the test tube.

Vhen a piece of calcium is placed in water (cold) it reacts vigorous-y giving out a bright light and heat as it does and so it wheezes ound the water in a circle.

When the ammonium chloride is warmed white dust flows from the mouth of the tube as it sublime into the air like a white eagle.

Use a stop watch and calculate the quantity of electricity in centimetres.

$$\frac{Time}{Weight} = electricity$$

'Describe and explain an experiment to show that hydrogen diffuses faster than air'
The gas (hydrogen) in bowl 1 had sucked the liquid up with it. The air, in bowl 2, was too heavy to suck up the liquid. This shows that hydrogen diffuses quicker than air.

Demonstration of diffusion
Place a pigs lung over the top of a gas jar then pump hydrogen into it and the same with oxygen. Then place each of them in a large glass dish sealing them off from the outside placing candles inside each of them after a while the H_2 container will pop but the O_2 candle will go out due to lack of air.

When carbon (Ca) is heated it will turn to a bubbly liquid because it is a solid. When iodine (Id) is heated it will give off a gas because it is a liquid.

Small amounts of impurities would get inside the expt. and cause nasty little happenings.